The Liberty Colouring Book

Introduction by
Sally Kelly

VIKING
an imprint of
PENGUIN BOOKS

VIKING

UK | USA | Canada | Ireland | Australia
India | New Zealand | South Africa

Viking is part of the Penguin Random House group of companies
whose addresses can be found at global.penguinrandomhouse.com.

First published 2015
001

Copyright © Liberty Retail Ltd, 2015
© Liberty Fabric Limited, 2015

The moral right of the author has been asserted

Designed by Couper Street Type Co.
Printed and bound in Italy by L.E.G.O. S.p.A.

A CIP catalogue record for this book is available from the British Library

ISBN: 978-0-241-24998-7

Introduction

In 1875, Arthur Lasenby Liberty began selling imported fabrics from Japan, Persia, India and China from a small shop on London's Regent Street. The popularity of these beautiful textiles meant the Liberty name soon became synonymous with a very distinct and highly fashionable style of fabric.

Today, Liberty's fabric division has a team of nine designers who work from a studio in Liberty's headquarters, Lasenby House. We produce a seasonal collection every six months, which is sold in the Liberty store, as well as to design houses and shops all over the world. We also design swimwear, childrenswear and menswear collections, work on collaborations with other designers and brands, and create bespoke designs for customers who are looking for their own exclusive Liberty print.

The process of bringing a design brief to a finished collection takes around two years and involves a number of stages along the way. We begin the design process by doing a research trip relevant to the brief – for example, the Gustav and Otto print on page 50 was inspired by a trip to Vienna. We are also constantly researching ideas by looking through the Liberty archive, visiting exhibitions and keeping up with trends in fashion and popular culture.

After the research trip and gathering of thoughts and ideas, we begin collecting imagery, sketching ideas and deciding on the materials we will use to create the designs. Each designer in our team has their own unique style, which means our collections appeal to a wide range of customers.

We will then spend two months intensively creating designs both in the studio and from home – wherever the inspiration flows best. Most of our designs are drawn, painted, carved or etched by hand before any work is done on the computer. When we are happy with the artwork, we scan the imagery on to the computer and work on putting the design into a repeat pattern so that it can be printed on large lengths of cloth. This is a crucial part of the design process, which ensures the patterns flow beautifully across the fabric and you can't see where the repeat begins and ends. Once the designs are ready, we send them to our printers, who produce samples for us to approve.

We then start to think about colour. We create at least six different colour palettes for each print, which will be used to colour up the designs in different options. We like to offer each design in at least three different colour ways. When the colour choices have been finalized, we send the whole collection to our printers. We then produce sample books for our wholesale customers from which they will place orders. The prints produced for the current fashion season will go into our archive of over 40,000 prints and in the future will become part of the classic Tana Lawn collection. We refresh the Tana Lawn collection every year by reviving our bestselling prints and colourways and introducing around five prints from the archive.

The Liberty Colouring Book is a celebration of the iconic, high-quality prints in Liberty's archive. We hope you will enjoy putting your own stamp on the prints we have chosen for this book as much as we have loved creating them.

It's time to lose yourself in Liberty paisleys and florals with this unique opportunity to reimagine our designs in your own personal style.

Sally Kelly
Designer
Liberty Art Fabrics

4

Busy Issie was created as a paisley pattern overlaid with delicate stylized flowers for the Autumn/Winter 2011 collection. It was inspired by Scott McKenzie's 1967 hit 'San Francisco'.

Ffion is a small-scale stylized floral print inspired by a simple wood-block design created for the Liberty archive in 1959. It has been added to the Liberty classic collection for Autumn/Winter 2016.

Christhl was part of the Spring/Summer 2011 collection and was inspired by illustrations in children's books.

Kitty Grace was inspired originally by an archive image. It was then re-created as a rock-star paisley to represent love songs as a part of the 'Liberty Rocks' print collection.

Caesar takes a fresh look at the classic peacock feather, a symbol of the Aesthetic Movement, which is closely associated with Liberty.

Poppy and Daisy is a stylized floral pattern designed by the Jack Prince Studio in 1974.

Originally designed as a furnishing fabric by
William Morris in 1883, **Lodden** was revived
for the Autumn/Winter 2007 collection.

Freya was taken straight from an admired 1930s
archive design and has now become part of the
classic Tana Lawn collection.

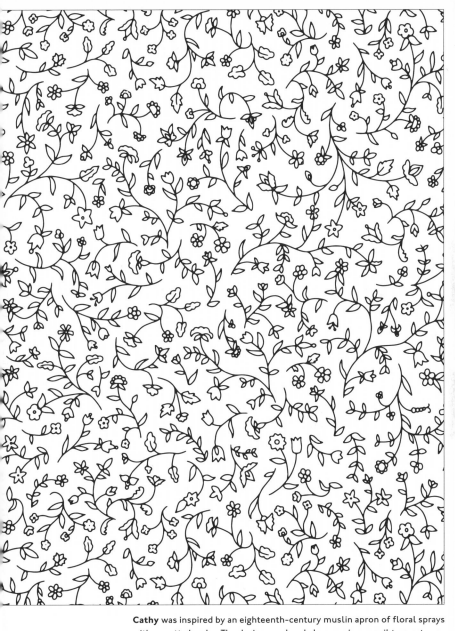

Cathy was inspired by an eighteenth-century muslin apron of floral sprays with a pretty border. The design was hand-drawn using pencil to create an all-over floral. It was part of the Autumn/Winter 2015 collection.

Based on a 1972 paisley print, **Jenny's Fan** was part of the *Alice's Adventures in Wonderland* themed collection for Spring / Summer 2015.

Lauren is a stylized floral print with waves of small flowers. It was part of the Spring/Summer 2006 collection.

Lola Weisselberg is a stylized floral pattern that was inspired by a children's book illustration. It was created for the Spring/Summer 2011 collection.

Hunter Paisley is a modern graphic paisley pattern that was part of the Spring/Summer 2009 collection.

Jess and Jean was created for the 'Gallery of Print' Spring/Summer 2014 collection, which took inspiration from each department in the store. Inspired by the beauty department, it was drawn using make-up rather than pencils and paint.

Koharu was created for the Japan-themed Autumn/Winter 2010 collection. It was inspired by Liberty's bestselling prints in the Japanese market.

Mabelle is a modern interpretation of a beautiful Indian chintz for the classic collection.

Tessa is typical of Liberty's collection of finely drawn and very detailed paisleys. It was developed from a very old paisley design in the Liberty archive and has been introduced to the Autumn/Winter 2016 classic collection.

Asaka was created by a Japanese
designer for the Spring/Summer
2014 collection.

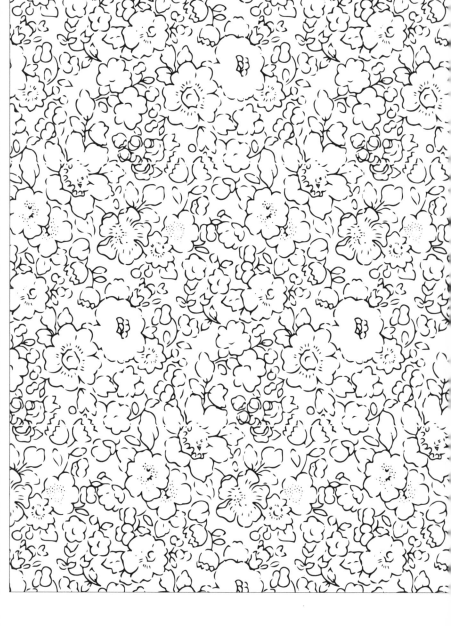

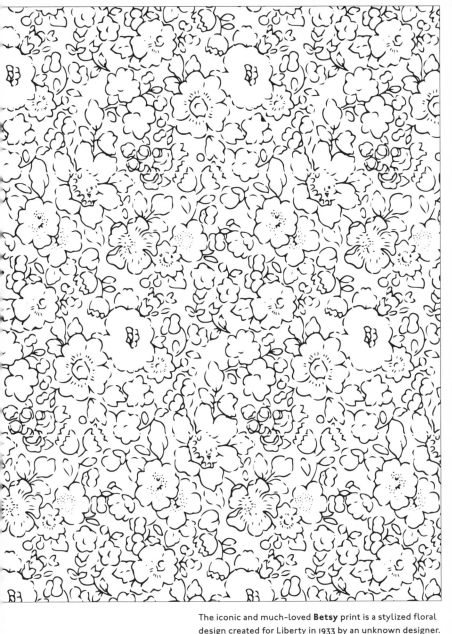

The iconic and much-loved **Betsy** print is a stylized floral
design created for Liberty in 1933 by an unknown designer.
It is one of the most popular classic designs.

Boadicea is a Toile de Jouy
print inspired by the archive
at the Whitworth museum.

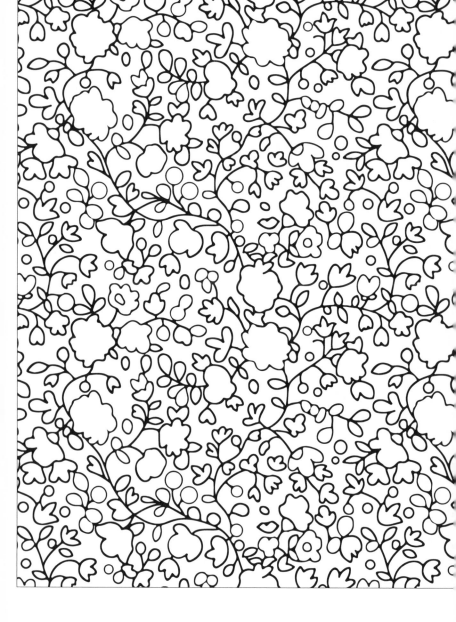

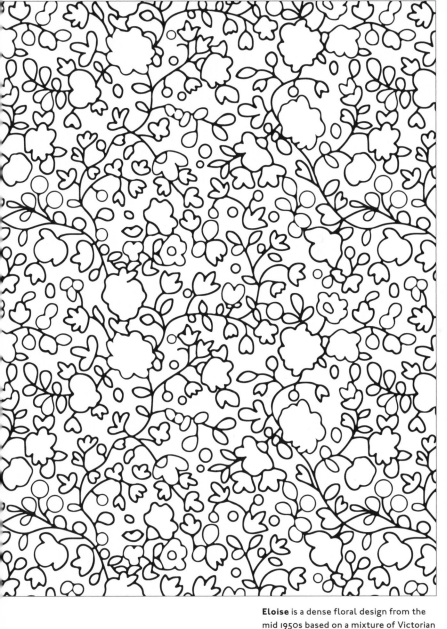

Eloise is a dense floral design from the mid 1950s based on a mixture of Victorian swatches in Liberty's old pattern books.

Originally created in the 1950s, **Mitsi** was reintroduced
to the collection in 2008 to represent designs from that
period. It now forms part of the classic collection.

The **Amy Jane** pattern of pretty hearts
with trailing flowers was part of the
Spring/Summer 2013 collection.

Gustav and Otto was inspired by a trip to Vienna
taken by the Liberty design team and the work of
artists in the Vienna Secession.

Created in-house, **Margaret Annie** is a detailed, hand-drawn print of summer perennials.

Over the Rainbow is a 1970s-inspired print that represents the magical imagination of children.

Glynis is based on apple blossom and was drawn from life in a garden orchard.

Toria was inspired by the wood carvings and plasterwork in and around the Tudor House, the home of Liberty's flagship store.

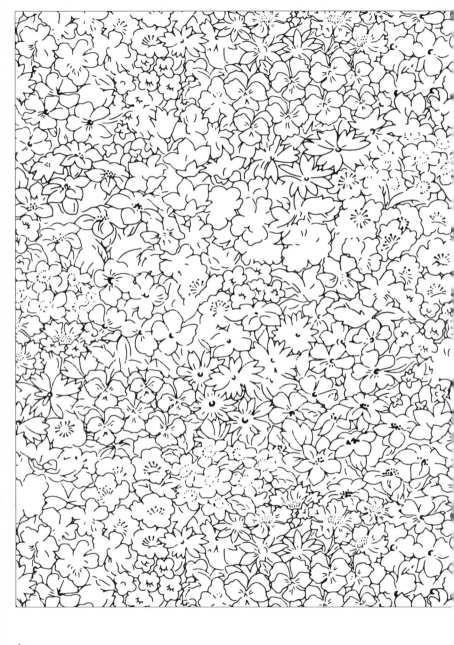

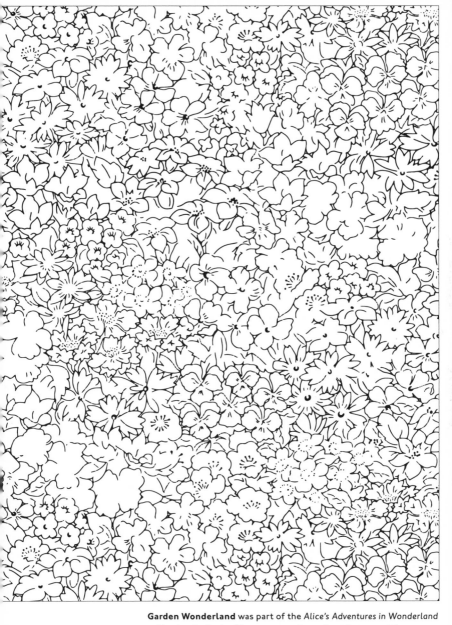

Garden Wonderland was part of the *Alice's Adventures in Wonderland* collection for Spring/Summer 2015. It was based on an archive painting and represents the garden of live flowers in the story.

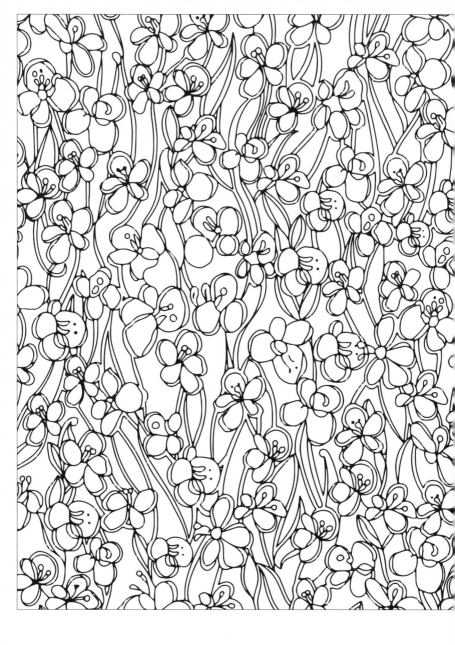

Jenny and Steve was part of the Spring/Summer 2014 collection and was inspired by an old photograph in the flagship store's restaurant, Café Liberty.

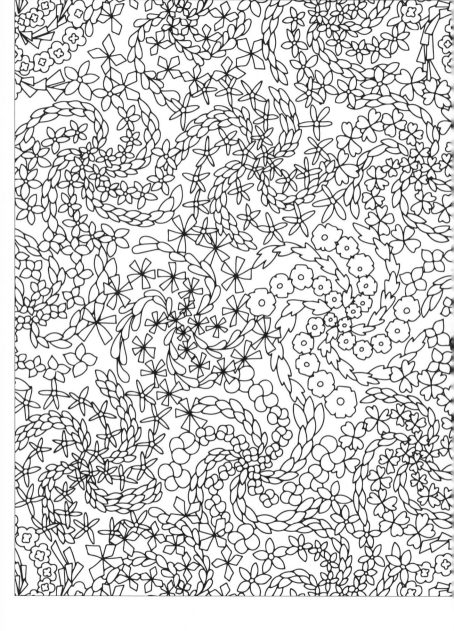

Angela Christina is a design from the Autumn/Winter 2013 collection. It is a finely drawn floral medley weaving between trailing vines of leaves.

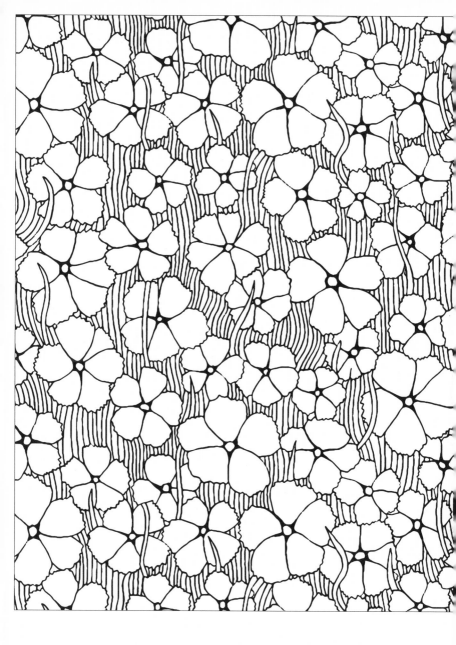

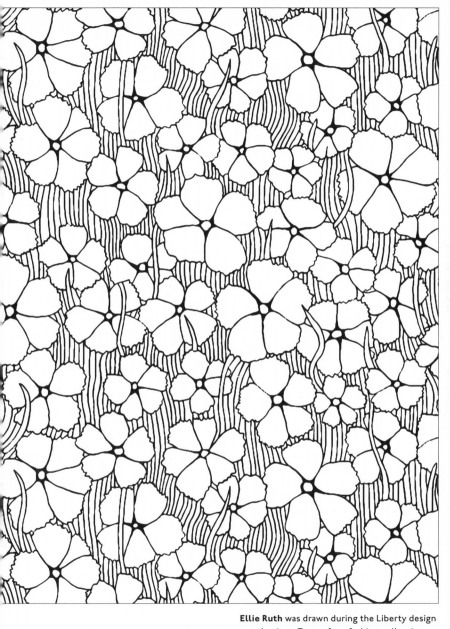

Ellie Ruth was drawn during the Liberty design team's trip to Tresco for a fashion collection inspired by the island for Spring/Summer 2012.

Charles has been reworked and rescaled from a Merton printworks archive block print.

Floral Fusion was created from the drawings of children from a school in south London.

Delilah Cavendish was part of the Spring/Summer 2014 fashion collection.

Now known as Tatum,
Juniper was derived from
1930s classic designs.

Edna was part of the Autumn/Winter 2014 'Wild Flowers'
fashion collection. It is a finely drawn, beautiful floral
with lily of the valley and trailing ivy.

Opie is a floral design inspired by tiles in a stately home in Scotland.

Capel is a one-colour floral that was first printed on
Tana Lawn in 1978. It is based on an old archive piece
and has been in the classic collection since 1993.

Diana is a modern
take on a floral Art
Nouveau print.

Based on a classic Liberty floral design
from the 1930s, **Danjo** was updated for the
Autumn/Winter 2012 Tana Lawn collection.

Eve is a miniature, hand-painted floral
pattern, inspired by the delicate prints
found on Liberty's casual and sleepwear.

Wiltshire is a leaf and berry pattern which was first created for Liberty in 1933 by an unknown designer and updated in 1968.

List of prints

28-29

Hunter Paisley is a modern graphic paisley pattern that was part of the Spring/Summer 2009 collection.

30-31

Jess and Jean was created for the 'Gallery of Print' Spring/Summer 2014 collection, which took inspiration from each department in the store. Inspired by the beauty department, it was drawn using make-up rather than pencils and paint.

32-33

Koharu was created for the Japan-themed Autumn/Winter 2010 collection. It was inspired by Liberty's bestselling prints in the Japanese market.

34-35

Mabelle is a modern interpretation of a beautiful Indian chintz for the classic collection.

36-37

Tessa is typical of Liberty's collection of finely drawn and very detailed paisleys. It was developed from a very old paisley design in the Liberty archive and has been introduced to the Autumn/Winter 2016 classic collection.

38-39

Asaka was created by a Japanese designer for the Spring/Summer 2014 collection.

40-41

The iconic and much-loved **Betsy** print is a stylized floral design created for Liberty in 1933 by an unknown designer. It is one of the most popular classic designs.

42-43

Boadicea is a Toile de Jouy print inspired by the archive at the Whitworth museum.

44-45

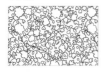

Eloise is a dense floral design from the mid 1950s based on a mixture of Victorian swatches in Liberty's old pattern books.

46-47

Originally created in the 1950s, **Mitsi** was reintroduced to the collection in 2008 to represent designs from that period. It now forms part of the classic collection.

48-49

The **Amy Jane** pattern of pretty hearts with trailing flowers was part of the Spring/Summer 2013 collection.

50-51

Gustav and Otto was inspired by a trip to Vienna taken by the Liberty design team and the work of artists in the Vienna Secession.

52-53

Created in-house, the **Margaret Annie** is a detailed, hand-drawn print of summer perennials.

54-55

Over the Rainbow is a 1970s-inspired print that represents the magical imagination of children.

56-57

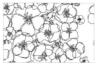

Glynis is based on apple blossom and was drawn from life in a garden orchard.

58-59

Toria was inspired by the wood carvings and plasterwork in and around the Tudor House, the home of Liberty's flagship store.

60-61

Garden Wonderland was part of the *Alice's Adventures in Wonderland* collection for Spring/Summer 2015. It was based on an archive painting and represents the garden of live flowers in the story.

62-63

Jenny and Steve was part of the Spring/Summer 2014 collection and was inspired by an old photograph in the flagship store's restaurant, Café Liberty.

64-65

Angela Christina is a design from the Autumn/Winter 2013 collection. It is a finely drawn floral medley weaving between trailing vines of leaves.

66-67

Ellie Ruth was drawn during the Liberty design team's trip to Tresco for a fashion collection inspired by the island for Spring/Summer 2012.

68-69

Charles has been reworked and rescaled from a Merton printworks archive block print.

70-71

Floral Fusion was created from the drawings of children from a school in south London.

72-73

Delilah Cavendish was part of the Spring/Summer 2014 fashion collection.

74-75

Now known as Tatum, **Juniper** was derived from 1930s classic designs.

76-77

dna was part of the Autumn/Winter 2014 'Wild Flowers' fashion collection. It is a finely drawn, beautiful floral with lily of the valley and trailing ivy.

78-79

Opie is a floral design inspired by tiles in a stately home in Scotland.

80-81

Capel is a one-colour floral that was first printed on Tana Lawn in 1978. It is based on an old archive piece and has been in the classic collection since 1993.

82-83

Diana is a modern take on a floral Art Nouveau print.

84-85

Based on a classic Liberty floral design from the 1930s, **Danjo** was updated for the Autumn/Winter 2012 Tana Lawn collection

86-87

Eve is a miniature, hand-painted floral pattern, inspired by the delicate prints found on Liberty's casual and sleepwear.

88-89

Wiltshire is a leaf and berry pattern which was first created for Liberty in 1933 by an unknown designer and updated in 1968.